Acknowledgement

The ideas in this book are drawn directly fr[c]
available from the Dementia Services Develop[...]
about our range of publications visit **www.dementiashop.co.uk**

Our design team includes lighting engineers and architects, optometrists
and occupational therapists, nurses, social workers and researchers and
a wide range of others whose aim in life is to improve things for people
with dementia and their carers. This publication represents the distillation
of their work and ideas and the ideas shared with us by people with
dementia and their carers. These people have been the world pioneers
in the area of dementia friendly design and architecture. This work is
dedicated to them.

Professor June Andrews
Colm Cunningham

Introduction 6

Basic principles

Specific Areas of the House

Conclusion 49

Useful reading 51

10 design hints to help people with dementia at home

By 'home' we mean the person's house where they have lived for a long time, or a new place to which they have moved because of frailty. So some of the ideas are about changes you can make, and some are about things you should look for if you are making a move.

People with dementia and those who live with them and who care about them have a lot to contend with. Some of the problems that they face every day in the places where we live, work and play are actually unnecessary. This book is intended as a handy guide to making things easier through making adjustments in your home or wherever a person with dementia is living, or being cared for. It can be read alongside *10 Helpful Hints for Carers: practical solutions for carers living with people with dementia*, which is part of this series.

Some of the ideas in this book cost virtually nothing. For example, people with dementia do much better when you increase the light levels, and it costs little to push back the heavy curtains, remove the unnecessary pelmet and take down any unneeded nets or blinds from the windows.

Other ideas will cost something, but it does not have to be a lot. For example, mirrors can be alarming for any person with dementia who does not recognise their reflection any more. Covering the bathroom mirror with a roller blind will remove the problem for the person with dementia without inconveniencing everyone else in the house.

Some of the ideas cost a lot of money. No one could afford to change all the carpets in the house just because of advice we give here, but if you have to change the carpets for another good reason, it is good to choose a floor covering that is 'dementia friendly'. It need not be more expensive and will look good too.

So not all of the suggestions in here are going to be attractive or even possible for you, but we offer them on the basis of experience about what works. You can decide to make any changes depending on how things are for you, and how affordable the idea is for you.

The ideas contained in this book are all based on research. In some cases the research has been done involving people with dementia, in others the ideas are taken from things that we know help people with other sorts of impairment. More ideas come from our direct experience of working with people with dementia and their carers throughout the world. If you are a researcher or want to look at where the published evidence is, you can find that through some of the literature that is mentioned at the end of the book.

More information can be obtained from the Dementia Centre website at www.dementia.stir.ac.uk and through the electronic library there and our online book shop www.dementiashop.co.uk. We have short courses on design for architects, designers and health professionals, and educational materials about assistive technology that you can download free of charge. There is more information about these at the end of this booklet.

10 hints on first principles

1. The first principle is to remember what well known problems the person with dementia may have. These may include

» difficulty in remembering things

» impairment in the capacity to work things out

» problems with learning new things

» the changes that often come with age, but a reduced ability to adapt to them

» great stress

Each of the ideas that we propose is based on understanding those fundamental problems. However, everyone is different, and the same person may have varied difficulties from time to time and even at different times of the day and night. There are not many hard and fast rules for any individual person or their home.

It is also important to remember that the person with dementia has many skills that may be overlooked. Dementia is not just about problems and difficulties.

> My granny was not able to remember if she had any milk or had eaten her dinner, but she taught me some really complicated knitting patterns that she learned when she was my age. She was amazing! She knitted socks for the sailors in the war when she was at school.

2. Memory problems are commonly associated with dementia, though people with dementia tell us that this was not the first thing that troubled them. Also, research indicates that for carers who support someone at home, the memory issues are not always the most troublesome feature of living with someone who has dementia.

But clearly it can be frustrating when a person has even mild memory problems. The pattern of memory loss is often that the person will forget more recent events, but remember earlier ones. Sometimes this causes complications. I might not know if I've seen my middle-aged daughter today, but I could still remember details of her time at school, including the names of all her little friends. There can also be a complication when the person with dementia has moved house in recent years.

> My dad would go for his walk and regularly turned up at the house where we used to live when I was a child. The lady there who bought the house off him twenty years ago was very reasonable, and would make him a cup of tea and ring me. That was lucky for us but still a bit embarrassing.

It is therefore a really fortunate thing if the person with dementia is spending as much of the rest of their life as possible in a place with which they have been familiar for a long time. Not having to try to remember new places makes life less stressful. But the time may eventually come when they do have to move, or it may be discovered that dementia is happening only after a move has been made. It is possible to make the best of this even then.

3. Another basic principle is to make it easy for the person with dementia to work things out. If we do this in public architecture and design it helps a wide range of people, including those with no cognitive impairment at all. Any of us can have a difficult moment when we are trying to find our way round an unfamiliar place. If you have lots of time it is not so bad. But if you have an appointment, or a deadline, a train to catch or just need the toilet, it can be really stressful. We can also be caught out by a non-standard bit of everyday equipment.

> " I rushed into the toilet in this really posh restaurant and had to stand with my legs crossed while I prodded the panels on the wall to work out where the closet doors were. I just made it, but when I went to wash my hands I could not work out how to turn on the tap, and ended up getting soaked because I turned it on too far and it went all over me. "

This lady did not have dementia, but was in a hurry for potentially embarrassing reasons. If you have dementia it is even harder to work things out, so the really important principle is to make everything dead obvious. A cross head tap is a very traditional design and most of us instinctively would know how to work it. A sign saying 'Ladies Toilet' might seem a bit mundane in an elegant restaurant, but it avoids the potential confusion caused by other fancy or subtle signs. A contrasting coloured door can be very stylish, and has the advantage of helping to prevent unpleasant incidents. Later sections will give other 'dead obvious' tips.

4. Try not to introduce new things for the person to learn, if it is not necessary.

> " At the hospital I asked the way to the Urology department and they said 'Follow the blue line on the floor.' There were three or four lines and anyway I forgot what line I was looking for and I saw someone in uniform. 'Can you please help me,' I said, 'I've got dementia and I'm supposed to be heading for Urology.' She assumed because I said the word 'dementia' that I didn't know what I was talking about and took me to Neurology. I nearly missed my appointment for the bladder problem. "

For finding the way in a public building, a more conventional method such as a sign on the wall with words and an arrow, repeated at intervals along the corridor would be more useful for people who can't easily retain new information. A picture is also useful (though we have tried and we can't think what picture you would use for urology!) Asking a person to memorise what a blue stripe means is a big thing if their basic problem is learning new things. If they must then retain that information for long enough to negotiate a busy building, you are making it tough for them for no good reason.

In the person's home, colour coding might be tempting as a subtle way of labelling drawers to help the person find things. But you are asking them to learn a new thing. They may well forget what the coloured labels mean, and still have to open the drawer to see what is there. A label with a picture of some socks or pants on it is not very subtle, but has the advantage of not requiring new learning, just eyes to see it.

5. This brings us on to the next hint. People with dementia are often older, and the older we are the more likely we are to have some impairments of eyesight or hearing, or a physical impairment.

For example, a person may have started to need glasses in order to see or a hearing aid to hear. Because of their dementia they may start to forget to put them on, or become apathetic about deciding to use them. When making adjustments in the home you must remember that this means the person may have difficulty in seeing and hearing. Even if they have got all they need, such as glasses or hearing aids, they may just leave them in a drawer. This means that some of the things in the house need to be made even more obvious than they were before. If your dad always had a bedside clock in the same place on the bedside table, get him another bigger one and put it in the same place. He'll still glance there for the time, but even without glasses, he'll be able to see it. What you are doing is reducing the need for him to remember things at a time when remembering might be harder. You are helping him to compensate for changes that a person without dementia would take in their stride.

6. All of the dementia problems described are very stressful. Just imagine how it feels to wake up in the morning and not know where you are. Maybe that has happened to you once or twice in your life after a great party, or when staying at a new hotel? In a few moments your head clears and you work out where you are because you see your clothes strewn about and you see clues in the room like your suitcase, car keys, invitation to the party etc. How stressed would you be if, after lying looking round for five minutes, or even running round the room looking out of the windows and trying doors you still could not work out where you are? It's a nightmare. The wildest ideas might occur to you. Am I a prisoner? Have I been drugged or abducted? Am I losing my mind? That is very stressful.

For the person with dementia, you might go through this every morning when you wake, if you are in a new place like a care home, or even if you have come to stay in your daughter's house. Even if you worked it out on Monday, you might have the same problem on Tuesday. This is why it's best to avoid making changes in the person's home, or if they have to move, make the place where they are to stay dead obvious. There will be more on this later, with hints on how to achieve that in each room of the house. However, you need to think about how to make the person less stressed and keep the atmosphere as calm as possible.

7. Find out from other people. There have been times in the past when doctors were reluctant to give a diagnosis of dementia because they thought that there was not much than could be done. This has changed a lot. They know that it helps relatives and friends care for someone with dementia if they are 'in the picture'. So if you know that the person has dementia, you are in a position to find out about what services are available locally. The best point of contact for this is often the local Alzheimer's organisation. Alzheimer's disease is one form of dementia, but even if you are not affected by that form of dementia, those organisations know what can help and what is available locally. In some places they have a free 24 hour helpline. But they also have websites, and information leaflets or drop-in centres where you can go to find out about what is available locally. If you attend their meetings you will meet other people who are going through the same journey as you. Don't travel alone! A list of these organisations can be found as the end of this book.

8. Keep a sense of humour. This is a tall order, but laughter is the best medicine for some of the problems that you will encounter. Sometimes when there is a problem that has arisen for design reasons – say a person goes into the wrong room at the wrong time and causes embarrassment – there is a temptation to shout and nag and try to get them not to do it again. Remember that the person with dementia is at the very point in their life when being told off or lectured to is going to make no difference at all, even if it ever did.

> Dad used to say to me, "Where is the bathroom? It used to be here!" and he'd point to the broom cupboard under the stairs. To begin with I'd argue with him. I think I thought if I could just get the facts to stick it would make him better. Now I just distract him and say, "Well, it is not there now... you need to go along here to the other room." I wonder sometimes if I'm insulting him by not keeping him right. I do try to laugh to myself. I am not laughing at him, but if I didn't stay cheerful I couldn't do my job of caring for him.

9. Things are always changing – we hope that there will be some new things for you in this book, but we are cheered up by the fact that scientists, engineers and all manner of clever technical people are listening to what you need and finding new ways of solving problems, so always be on the look out for new products and ideas. You can often get them from your local Alzheimer organisation, your community psychiatric nurse, or the social work department.

10. It is never too soon to start. Even in middle age we may be making decisions about our homes, like a new bathroom or kitchen, or new carpets. Have half an eye to the question of how that will be for you when you are older, and if you have memory problems. Don't worry, most people won't get dementia. But dementia friendly houses can be just as comfortable and fashionable as any other, so why would you not choose for your future comfort?

10 hints on lighting and sound

1. Older people need much more light in order to see than young people. The explanation lies in the changes in the ageing eye. The cornea, which is the clear part at the front, becomes more yellow as time goes by. It has been described as if, each year, an older person goes round with a thicker pair of yellow goggles on. You can still see, and you might not notice the difference yourself, but the truth is that you are not seeing subtle contrasts any more, and sometimes not able to do certain things as a result. You might not be able see to read or sew, and tell your family, "I can't do those things anymore." In reality you could, if the circumstances including light level were fixed for you. In addition, older eyes are slower at adjusting to changes in the light level. The good news is that there is a quick solution – more light!

2. Even if the room seems quite bright in day time there are simple things you can do to brighten it up. Cut back garden foliage from round the windows or trim trees that block the light. Paint any exterior wall outside the window white, so that it can reflect light back into the room. Clean the windows, and think about whether the nets and blinds are doing anything useful. If they are reducing glare in the room from direct sunlight, you may need to hang on to them for those moments. Depending on where you live, and the direction of the windows, that might not be very often.

3. Being green and saving energy is important, and we've all got energy saving light bulbs. For an older person, it is important to note that those bulbs lose their luminosity over time and you need to have a routine of changing them about once a year. This is particularly important in places where there is a transition from light to dark. Going into their hallway or stairwell, the person may be dependent on light to avoid a fall. The light may take a few seconds to reach full luminosity, and even then it might not be as bright as it used to be. You don't want them to be hovering at the top of the stairs in half dark.

4. It has been said that you can add to the confusion of the person at home by changing a lot of things. If you make only one change, go in and increase the number and wattage of the lights in the house. You have to check the maximum tolerance of the old shades and fittings in order to avoid a fire. If there is one pendant light, you may be able to replace that with one of the branched pendants that holds three or five bulbs. You have not changed much in the room, but you have made everything that is there much clearer to the person.

5. Daylight is particularly important for people in setting your body clock. The body clock is what creates the normal rhythms in a day, and that includes when you might feel like going to sleep or getting up. People with dementia sometimes turn night into day and so it is important to support them in keeping to the same pattern as the rest of us....not least because we need to sleep, even if they don't seem to at times. It is important to make the home open to daylight in order to help with this balance. If it is a dark little flat with few windows, you might consider practical ways in which you can make sure that the person gets outside regularly. There is more on this in the garden section of this book.

6. Noise is another element of the environment that needs attention. People with dementia have a hard time thinking and working things out. We all know how hard it is to concentrate properly when there is an irritating noise in the background. We say, "Turn it down! I can't hear myself think!" The person with dementia has an impaired capacity to think, so we need to give them all the help we can. One important thing is to clear up the noise in the background. Having the TV or radio on when no one is watching or listening is unnecessary, but it happens a lot because most people stop noticing it. This meaningless noise could be quite disabling for a person who is already easily confused. Turning it off can help the person with dementia to think more clearly.

> The psychiatrist and I went to see a lady with dementia and she was in the living room with her daughter. The television was on, and he said to the daughter, 'Do you mind? The TV is a bit distracting.' She replied, 'Shall I change the channel for you? There's sport on the other side.' She really did miss the point.

7. Hearing properly helps people to make sense of the world, and older people with dementia probably have some hearing changes associated with their age. If the person with dementia can't hear properly they may become angry and frustrated and this can lead to disturbing behaviour. You need to support the person to hear as well as possible with regular hearing checks and making sure that they have the right hearing aids and that they are working. You may have to learn how to work the hearing aid so that you can help them. You can also make changes to the 'acoustic environment' that will help. The basic principle of those changes is to increase sound and reduce noise. Sound is information that comes to us through our ears, and noise is interference with that information. In other parts of this book we have spoken about 'decluttering' the visual environment. You can also 'declutter' the auditory environment. You want to help the person to hear important things. Hearing aids can be problematic. Controls may be small and difficult to manage, so it is worth everyone learning how to fix them so they can help. It is important to make sure that the person has not got wax blocking their ears. The person may appear more confused because they are not answering you and look puzzled, when in fact they are not hearing you. There is evidence that people build up more ear wax if they have lost their back teeth, so we need to be alert to this and get it checked out, particularly if those teeth have gone.

8. Soft furnishings such as curtains and cushions help to absorb noise. Of course, as advised elsewhere, you need to avoid making changes in the person's home if they have lived there for a long time. But if they have moved into another place, such as a relative's house or a new apartment of their own, remember the value of soft furnishings. Sometimes it is imagined that the person may suffer from continence issues, and a nice wood or vinyl floor may seem easier for hygiene. There are carpet tiles and floor coverings available that can be cleaned and kept odour free, and they will reduce the amount of clattering from the movement of furniture and clopping of feet. There is more on this in the section on floor coverings. If the person has a hearing aid, this reduction in noise is really important, as meaningless squeaks are magnified just as fiercely by a hearing aid as helpful and encouraging words. It makes it harder to concentrate on something purposeful or pleasant like some music or the afternoon play on the radio.

9. Windows – hearing noises from outside may be welcome so it is important that the person has the capacity to open and close windows so that they can choose. Elsewhere in this document we describe how important it is for the person to have access to sunlight. Daylight is good for setting the body clock and that can happen through windows. However, a window will exclude the important sun rays that will help the person to manufacture vitamin D, which is vital for bone strength and also helping with falls. There is more about this in the section on balconies. However, in the meantime, don't forget that windows are a significant source of interesting sounds and annoying noise. Being able to open and shut them gives the person with dementia the chance to demonstrate which is which, from their own point of view. Choosing a seat for the person near a window with a low sill is also good as the person can see more of what is happening. If the person has to look up the way to see out the window they might only see the clouds and sky, and nothing more interesting.

10. If you have good concentration you can probably ignore things that are going on around you. If you want to check whether there is unnecessary noise in the house that might be distracting, sit still for a few minutes with your eyes shut, and focus on what you can hear. If you are anxious you will be more alert, and notice more noise. Remember to listen to things from the point of view of an anxious person who has difficulty screening out extraneous noises. Then you will be able to work out how to make the environment less noisy. It can be as simple as maintenance on plumbing to help reduce knocking in pipes.

10 hints on decoration and floor coverings

1. As with most of the hints, there are two variations – what you should do if the person with dementia has stayed in the place for years, and what works well from our experience when they have moved to a new place. If you make changes in a place with which the person is familiar, they may thank you for your efforts. However, in a relatively short time, they may not remember when or how the changes took place and will be puzzled with the change in their environment, as if it happened overnight.

> Mum had a horrible old sofa and chairs which showed the wear and tear of years of family and pets and we bought her a new suite for her birthday. She came to the shop and chose it with us. Then weeks later she called me up, in some distress, wanting to know what had happened in her house because her suite was gone and had been replaced with something else.

If the person has moved to a new place, everything is new, and this is when the principle applies that everything should be dead obvious. This really means 'traditional' or 'what the person was used to in the past'. An example of this in fixtures is plumbing: cross head taps are more traditional than some of the smooth, sleek continental designs that we now see in the show rooms.

2. People with dementia will walk more swiftly and safely over a smooth matte self-coloured surface. What does this mean in practical terms? It means that if you are in a position to choose the floor covering where a person with dementia is going to stay, you pick one colour and stick with it all the way through the building, through kitchen, bathroom and living areas. It is very helpful at the threshold between two rooms to make the carpet bar (also called a trim) the same colour as the flooring.

This can reduce the risk of the person thinking it is an object in their path that they need to step over. In areas where you need a hard surface rather than a carpet, as in the kitchen, you need to have a floor covering that is not shiny and reflective. The person with dementia may believe that this is wet and slippery and will alter their gait when walking over it, leading to problems of speed and stability.

The steps of a staircase should contrast with the staircase frame and walls. This will help the person see their way. As mentioned earlier, lighting is really important on the stair to avoid the risk of the person seeing what might look like shapes or holes that they are hesitant to put their feet on.

3. If the person is in their own home with a familiar carpet they are less likely to have a problem with an otherwise unpromising pattern. We rarely look where we are going in our own home – which is why we can find our way around in near dark. You need to have a look out for trip hazards and remove them, notwithstanding the danger that the person will later hunt for them. Remember that one trip hazard on the floor can be the slippers or other footwear that the person wears around the house.

4. Where there is a choice, finish the traditional skirting boards around any room in a colour that contrasts with doors and walls, which will help the person with dementia to see where the floor ends and the wall begins. Depth and colour perception are diminished as the years pass, so this colour contrast can be really helpful for orientation. There is a tendency in wet areas such as bathrooms to make the walls and floor the same colour – so it is a good idea to specify this contrast in particular in those areas.

5. If a ramp is being introduced to help the person to get about on different levels, it should be finished in a material that is slip resistant. However, the person may well need to shuffle, so it must not be so resistant that it prevents shuffling. Ramps should have a kerb on exposed edges or a brightly visible toe guard.

19

6. There is a body of literature about colour and how it can affect mood. This booklet does not intend to comment on that. Colour is also a matter of taste and association, and preferences may be highly individual. The most important message about colour from this book is about the importance of contrast. If you want to test whether the colour of the chairs contrasts with the carpet, make a black and white photocopy of the two colours together and see how easy it is to tell them apart. Remember what has been said about the ageing eye. The person with dementia may have these problems on top of all their other concerns, so it is a good idea to give as much help as possible. Don't make it hard to work out where the chair is! If you think the chair does not contrast, you can change it with one from another room that does. Alternatively you can put a throw on the chair, but be careful that there is no cloth hanging that the person may catch their foot on.

7. Patterns which represent real life can be problematic. If you have representative patterns such as leaves or flowers the person with dementia may think they are real and try to pick them up or pick them off. Of course *trompe l'oeil* (or confuse the eye) features have their place.

©iStock.com/Creasence

For example with an exit door that you don't want someone to use, you can paint it the same colour as the surrounding wall, and paint a 'skirting board' along the bottom to trick the eye into not seeing it. However, we have seen examples where people paint a fireplace on a wall, where a real fire has been condemned as too risky. People with dementia are clinging to reality so you need a really good excuse to justify any 'tricks', and there are much better solutions than a painting of a fire. For example, a fire surround can be obtained with false coals and a rotating light which is exactly like the one you might buy for normal use, except that it does not have a radiant heat source. It could be mounted on a wall, or over a radiator with a fan to push out warm air.

8. In the light of what we say about light...curtains should be of light coloured material. This will reflect light in the day, and at night when they are closed, will avoid the dimming effect of most of one wall being covered in dark cloth.

9. We do get asked at the Dementia Centre about whether there are certain colours that might be used in art, or subjects that are more suited for hanging on walls. From what we know at this time, it really is a matter of taste, in the person's own home or their own space in someone else's home.

> I took all of mum's pictures to be with her when she moved from the old house to the new flat. Every wall seemed to be covered, but she liked that, having her friends and family around her, and it certainly gave us things to talk about when we visited her.

10. Bed linen and towels can be used to maximise contrast and improve the chances of things being seen and used. There is more on this in the section on bedrooms and the section on bathrooms.

10 hints on assistive technology

1. Assistive technology is the expression we use for the gadgets that you can buy that will help the person with dementia around the house. We like some of them so much that we think everyone should have them. They deal with common problems that every one might have. The difficult thing for the person with dementia is that they might have more difficulty with some of those problems, so they really benefit from the help that the gadgets give. You may be able to buy some of these within your own budget, or your local authority may have a department that is able to advise you or provide you with them. An important feature is that lots of brainy scientists and engineers are inventing new applications all the time, so don't rely on this book. Search on the web to find out what the latest is.

2. One of the common problems that the person with dementia has in their own home is the extent to which everyone else is anxious about them and whether they will have an accident or cause an accident. Many of the ordinary accident prevention or detection things that are used in most homes must be brought into play especially when the person has dementia. For example, make sure that there is a smoke alarm fitted and working with the batteries properly fitted.

3. A common worry is that the person will leave the house at an inappropriate time. There is a range of approaches including monitoring when the person leaves, or warning a carer or call service that they are leaving, or tracking them so that they can leave when they like and no one is too worried because the person will be found easily if they don't come home. Tracking gives the person most freedom and is not a design issue. There are commercial products which can be attached to detect opening of the external doors of the house. This can be monitored by a call centre, a carer at a distance, or through a pager or sonic message to the other people in the house.

4. Infra red beam emitters have a variety of useful functions, from turning on lights when the person enters or leaves an area to alerting the carer to the fact that the person with dementia is on the move.

5. Computer technology which is familiar to many parents and grandparents allows families to see each other and speak to each other on their personal computers over the internet. There are products based on this principle which are available commercially, so that families at a distance can talk to the person with dementia and see how they are doing for themselves. They may also allow the carer at a distance to unlock a drawer with a crucial item, such as a spare key, so the person can access duplicates of lost items rather than relatives having to travel to their home at an inconvenient time to help them search.

6. People get worried about the cooker and whether the person with dementia will switch it off. It is possible to arrange the cooker so that it cannot be switched on randomly by the person in the house and so that it switches itself off. Smoke and heat detectors do have their place, but it is problematic if the person with dementia does not understand the alarm and fails to exit the house in an emergency.

7. Medication alerts come in a variety of forms, including one which recognises when the person opens their pill box, and alerts a carer if the box has not been used within the right time frame. It can also lock up unused doses of medication to prevent the person from accidentally overdosing.

8. Assistive technology includes a wide range of checking mechanisms where a fall detector can alert a call centre that will make verbal contact with the person and send someone round if there is a problem. A movement sensor in the bed can alert someone if the person is moving too little for too long. The alarm that is sounded can be a vibrating alarm under the carer's pillow so that the whole house is not roused in the night.

9. There are inventions that have been shown to us at the Dementia Centre which we want in our own homes now. One is a plug which automatically drains away the water when the sink or bath gets too full, thus preventing floods. We all wanted to buy one for our upstairs neighbours. Another is a bar code reader that would tell the microwave exactly what setting was needed to cook the instant meal. We find reading the instructions and peering at the dials too exhausting after a day's work. If you need a microwave meal, you're probably feeling too tired to cook or you are in a hurry. We also liked an auditory device that asked us whether we had our keys on us as we went through a door.

10. It is important to remember that assistive technology is not without its problems. It has to be purchased and maintained, and the person has to consent to it being used in their own home. Some of the devices are possibly annoying or even extremely disconcerting. If you have always lived alone the voice asking you about your keys could be spooky, particularly if you have forgotten about the installation of the device. Some of the inventions are brilliant, but they can only be one part of the solution to the challenge of maintaining the dignity and independence of the person with dementia.

Specific areas of the house

10 hints on the bedroom

The main aim of the bedroom is for the person to sleep and relax. It is also usually where you store your clothes, dress and undress. Of course some people also have it as an entertainment zone, with laptops and televisions, and radios. It is a place where people have traditionally enjoyed some of their most intimate moments. Each person must have it their own way. Sleep is very important in dementia. The person with dementia may suffer from a crushing exhaustion. There are circumstances that sometimes mean they turn night into day, and stay up at night. This is exhausting for carers. The principles that help a decent night's sleep still apply, but there are some interesting twists.

1. Avoid making unnecessary changes in the person's own home as they will be familiar with what is there. As explained in the first section on basic principles, the person is not good at learning new things when they have dementia. If you get rid of the old armchair beside the bed, even with their consent, they might be troubled the next day, wondering where it is and if someone stole it from them. If you are expecting the person to sleep in a brand new environment, design it in such a way that you can help maintain the skills that the person still has for as long as you can. So you need to keep everything in the bedroom as familiar as possible. This usually means traditional or conventional but either way it means SIMPLE.

2. A common reason for people waking in the night is needing to go to the toilet. You want to make this as simple and convenient as possible. This is because if the person becomes confused about where to go they might wet themselves before they get to the toilet, or have another accident such as falling over in the rush to get there. Some people get offered a commode (which is a mobile toilet) that can be place beside the bed for night time use. Even though a commode chair beside the bed might seem convenient when the person has a mobility problem, it is an unfamiliar

piece of equipment which the person might find hard to remember. Then they'll walk past it on the way to find the loo. An ensuite toilet is ideal, and should be part of any hospital or care home design. People have them at home also, in some new homes, and there are some ensuite dementia basic ideas that are covered in more detail in the section on toilets and bathrooms. If there is an ensuite toilet, position the head of the bed so that the person can see the toilet when resting.

In the absence of an ensuite toilet, the person can be encouraged and supported to find the toilet by making the way easy to find. The toilet light could be left on all night. The problem is that if this is a new departure, the person with dementia may get up and switch it off, thinking that someone has forgotten it. Another solution is to have something that automatically switches the light on when the person starts to move about. There is a range of easy to install, inconspicuous devices that can do this, from wall mounted movement sensors to pressure mats. They are less complicated than you would think. There is more about these in the section on toilets.

3. Sleep is very important because the condition of dementia is in itself exhausting. It is also important for carers that the person they care for does sleep at night in order to give the carer peace to sleep. We know that not getting enough sleep is bad for health, and a carer already has a lot to contend with. If the person with dementia turns night into day, or leaves the house in the middle of the night, it is distressing and exhausting for everyone. There is no great inherent harm in the person with dementia being awake at night as long as they get enough sleep in 24 hours. However, it is unsupportable for those with whom they live who have to worry about the safety and supervision of the person, and their own health and wellbeing.

It is natural for humans to sleep in the dark, though some of us can sleep in lots of different light levels, if we are tired and relaxed enough. For people with dementia to sleep well it is important to control the amount of light and the sort of light to which they are exposed at night.

For example, if there is light somewhere in the building, the person with dementia may be described as 'wandering' at night, when they are actually sensibly going to investigate the light. This could have bad consequences if it is an outside light that has been switched on by a movement sensor. It might tempt the person to leave the house to have a look, and then you have a person outside in their nightclothes at risk of cold, or getting lost and distressed.

A truly beneficial light would be one in the toilet as described in the previous section. You can use a movement sensor or passive infrared beam to switch on the toilet light at any time when the person starts to get out of bed. With any luck, they will use the toilet and go back to bed, because there is nothing else distracting or vaguely interesting in the rest of the house, or outside.

4. Storing clothes in drawers and cupboards in your bedroom is sensible and traditional. However, if the person with dementia has access to their whole wardrobe it can be overwhelming. If there are too many clothes there can be a range of choices that leads to the person not being able to decide. One solution is to choose to lay out the clothes for the next day the night before, or come in and do that in the morning. This serves to encourage the person with dementia to dress themselves with the clothes that are there. You can have a wardrobe that has one glazed door and one wooden door. If you put the clothes that have been chosen for the next day behind the glazed door, hanging there, clear and obvious, it is easy for the person to take them out and put them on. All the unnecessary things are out of sight. It is not unknown for a person with dementia to put on more than one of each item…you can make that less likely if only one of everything is in view. You can even get a wardrobe with a light inside, to illuminate the right clothes. The decision about what to wear can be done well in advance, with the cooperation of the person with dementia, reflecting their wishes.

5. Make sure that everything looks like what it is supposed to be. This is easier at home. In one care home we visited one wall of the room had a very attractive bank of wooden doors. Behind one was the wardrobe, another was the door to the ensuite shower room, and another was a wooden panel which disguised some irrelevant architectural features including a fuse box and the reverse side of an alcove from the next room. The person using the room was faced with a wall of wood, and often opened the wrong door, or tried to open the wooden panel. The potential for confusion continued as the exit door of the room was the same size and colour as these other doors.

If this is the set up in the home where they have always lived, the person with dementia will probably manage it for a long time. Remember the principle of changing as little as possible of what is familiar. If it has been a new design feature in their house, it might start to be confusing as their recent memories fade. Having said that you need the room to be as dark as possible at night, you can introduce more light during the day to help them to remember their way around and find things.

Confusion can further occur at night for the person with dementia if the carer is dressed in day clothes. If you remind the person that it's time to go to bed and you are in day clothes, this may not make sense to them. Pointing out that it is dark outside may not be enough. They may think that they are missing out on something that is happening in the house or that you are going to go out. If you need to be in your day clothes putting a dressing gown over them may help to give consistent messages about it being time to sleep.

6. You can use signs. At one time we worried about whether this was unnatural or contrary to culture, making the person's own living space seem institutionalised. Most of us don't have a sign on our top drawer saying 'socks and pants' – tempting though it might be in a teenager's bedroom. However, dementia is extraordinary, so we need to take extraordinary measures at times to help the person make the best of their remaining independence. People with dementia will tell you that they make signs for themselves when they are finding their own practical solutions. We can help as well even if this includes putting signs up in the person's own space. We need to emphasise what is practical and what helps, even if it seems at first to offend the eye. A sign with words can be enhanced or replace by a picture. A picture of some socks might be helpful if the person is starting to lose vocabulary or finding it difficult to read. Signs on doors should be at the right height for the person. We recommend that the base of the sign is no higher than 4 feet/122cm from the floor.

7. As we get older, our eyesight deteriorates. It has two effects, one of which affects our diurnal rhythms, also known as the 24 hour body clock. You will notice as you get older that you may need glasses for the first time, or different glasses from those you had before. You will need more light for basic tasks that you once did easily, like reading the small print, or threading a needle, or cutting your toenails. This is partly explained by a yellowing of the cornea, mentioned in the '10 hints on first principles' section of this book.

In addition to stopping you doing close work without specs, that yellowing seems to prevent daylight from falling onto the back of the eye. When night and day get mixed up, for example when you travel to a different time zone, people suffer from jet lag which is a horrible feeling. You may feel sick and tired in the day time and ready for action in the middle of the night. In older people who do not get out much in daylight, the body clock gets upset, and they want to be out and about in the middle of the night, disrupting everyone's sleep. So this helpful hint for the bedroom is one which says, "Go out in daylight whenever you can in the day time."

8. Colour in the bedroom - For the ageing eye, colour contrast is very important, so resist the attractive pastel colours that will blend into each other. Patterns in the wallpaper can cause difficulty. Our brains work by making sense of the visual information round us. With the constant striving to find a pattern, we sometimes see things that are entertaining. Did you ever see a cloud that looked like a dog, and entertain the children by pointing it out? Have you seen a face on the full moon? The cognitive impairment in dementia, combined with poor lighting and the ageing eye means that a person may lie in bed and stare at the wallpaper and believe that they are seeing something that is not there. It could be disturbing. This is particularly important with a mirror in the bedroom as this can pick up the subtle movement of a curtain and the person may confuse this for someone being in the room. If the person with dementia begins to report that there is someone in their room try covering their mirror at night.

A plain, matte, self-coloured surface on the floor covering is also useful, if possible contrasting with the wall. You can't change everything, and must be careful what you change at home, but even a nice bright contrasting set of bed linen can make the bed more obvious.

It is important to say that it's not a good idea to redecorate the house of the person with dementia in many cases. You might feel you should brighten it up by redecorating. They might be delighted when they come back from their trip away and find you have done it. But the next morning they may wake up and have forgotten that you did it. Lying in a bedroom that is the right shape but with the wrong décor, they may come to the conclusion that they are in a neighbour's house, and try to get 'back home, next door'.

9. Sound is an issue in the bedroom. In care homes sometimes people with dementia get up and 'wander' in the night. You need to ask "Is it quiet at night?" The staff may think so, but they may forget the nurse call system that operates with a buzzer going off a few times an hour, sometimes for two or three minutes. And that the washing is done at night and the tumble dryer is rumbling away. Or that the rubbish bin with a foot pedal you use many times an hour clangs shut with a bang when you take your foot off the pedal. That is all before the old man shouts, "What's that noise? I can't sleep for the racket!" and wakes everyone else up. Design solutions in care homes include silent nurse call systems that operate with vibrating pagers to alert the nurse that someone has pulled the cord and needs help. The Royal College of Nursing once estimated that one in seven women has worked in nursing at some point in their life. If you have noisy buzzers in a care home, we'll all be out of bed trying to find who needs our help. Get them silenced now!

In their own house, even if it is nice and quiet, the slightest unfamiliar noise can disturb the person with dementia. If I still live in my own home there are louder noises at night which, because they are well known to me, don't keep me awake. The familiar sound in the pipes of the central heating as it cools down, the creak of the floorboard outside the bathroom and the click of the light switch when someone uses it in the night are part of the soundscape that actually soothes me to sleep. The roar of the first flight out of the airport may make me turn over and go to sleep again when at home, but in an unfamiliar setting I might lie and wonder what is making soft unfamiliar noises.

10. Security at night is a problem for some people. The carer may be afraid to go to sleep in case the person with dementia wakes up and leaves the premises. There is a range of really useful alarms which won't wake the whole household. For example, you can buy a very simple passive infrared beam emitter which will fix to the bedroom wall with a small velcro adhesive patch. When the beam is broken it can set off a small vibrating alarm under the carer's pillow.

> I can have a deep sleep now every night because I know I'll get woken when mum gets out of bed, and sometimes she goes for a week without doing it. I used to lie half awake all night waiting for the crash of the front door.

10 hints on bathrooms and toilets

1. Incontinence can be an issue for people with dementia. It is not however, inevitable. In many cases it is a result of not being able to find the toilet and use it in time. The person is older and not so quick on their feet. They may have a bit of a reduction in their capacity to 'hold on'. One of the aims of dementia friendly design at home is to make sure that even if the person forgets where things are they can easily find them. Clearly the toilet is easier to find and use if it can be seen from a wide range of angles, e.g. from both the hall and the bedroom. You may not have a choice in your home, but if you did, you'd want to position the toilet in a place that is as obvious and easy to find as possible.

2. For night time, as described in the section about the bedroom, an ensuite toilet is ideal. Position the bed so that the lavatory can be seen from the head of the bed. This means that when the person wakes in the night, they are in a position to see where it is, so that they can use it independently. You can enhance this possibility by switching on the toilet light with a movement sensor, or by having a little night light on all the time to make sure that it can be seen when needed. You'll notice that in most standard hotel rooms exactly the opposite occurs, and the toilet is discreetly positioned where you won't see it when you are in bed. We need to be more "out" about the need to go to the loo.

3. Bathrooms and toilets almost always have a mirror to help with grooming tasks like shaving and putting on makeup. Unfortunately, with dementia, a person may reach a stage where they do not recognise their own reflection. Have you ever heard someone say that they felt they were starting to look like their father or mother?

> I was in the town centre and glancing up I thought I saw my mother coming in the other direction. On a second look I realised it was myself in a full length mirror! (Peals of laughter)

34

It is not funny if the person reaches a stage where they have no recognition of the face in the mirror. Using their logic, they will assume that they are looking at a stranger, and that stranger is looking right back at them, with a puzzled, perhaps unfriendly expression. The mirror has become a window through which a strange person can spy on them. In a place like the toilet where people need maximum privacy, this can have disastrous effects. Hints for dealing with mirrors range from banning them (which is hard on the rest of the household) to treating them like a window and having a little curtain or roller blind that can be closed when the person with dementia is using the space.

Confusion should also be avoided with use of toilet and bath mats. These often contrast with the floor in the bathroom and may be perceived as a barrier the person has to step over.

> Jean stopped going near the bath and would not get in. Her husband could not understand why as she used to find a bath very relaxing. One evening when trying to help her into the bath he realised that he forgot to put the bath mat down. Jean got in to the bath without a problem. After that Jean's husband stopped putting the bath mat down before she got into the bath and only set it in front of the bath when Jean was ready to get out of the bath.

4. Light has been emphasised as being really important for supporting people to be self caring, but you need to be careful about other reflective surfaces in bathrooms, as glare can present a problem for the ageing eye. You may be able to use blinds or nets to reduce glare, but make sure that there is plenty of light. Another reflective surface is the window, so at night, when lights are on inside and not outside, the window may act as a mirror and create disturbing reflections for the person with dementia. Think carefully about the lighting arrangements overnight, in order to allow visibility of the toilet without disturbing sleep.

5. Handrails should be robustly fixed, comfortable to touch and contrast in colour with the walls to be easily visible. If handrails are being fitted as a safety feature in your home, you can remind whoever is doing it that they don't always come in grey and white but are available in a wide range of contrasting colours in order to help the person see them. Using a contrasting hand or bath towel to the wall colour may also help the person with dementia locate and use this.

6. Do use taps that are traditional in appearance and simple to operate with clear indications of hot and cold. For older people who have lived in the UK for a long time, the mixer tap is a relatively new invention. It is potentially a safety feature, allowing you to run water over your hands that is not too hot or too cold, but you may need to think of another way of controlling the temperature of the hot water supply, because the mixer tap may be confusing.

The WC seat and lid should be a contrasting colour to the pan and other surroundings to assist in positioning for sitting down to use the toilet, and also for direction for men standing to use the toilet. The person will be familiar with their own toilet, but if they are moving to a new place, and there is a choice, traditional cisterns are easier to understand. Toilet roll holders can sometimes be hard to find if they are on the wall behind the seat and the person has restricted mobility or vision. A good idea is a free standing toilet roll holder. The first one I ever used was made for me about thirty years ago by a hospital handyman out of a free standing ashtray. Necessity is the mother of invention. If you have any good inventions, let us know for the next edition of this book. Choosing toilet paper that contrasts with the wall and holder will also help the person find this and use it. The quality of the toilet paper may matter as if it is hard for the person to find the end of the roll they may get frustrated or give up.

8. The floor finish needs to be non-slip, and also not shiny. Shiny floors look as if they might be wet. This can reduce the confidence and therefore the mobility of the person using the room. The colour of the threshold to the room and the colour of the floor covering both outside and inside the room should be as close to each other as possible.

9. In every case think about traditional features, such as a plug and chain rather than a lever for plugholes. Surfaces to display soaps and useful things help orientate the person. Think of what the person would have been used to in primary school. The person might 'see' a bar of soap and 'miss' a soap dispenser.

If your bathroom is already decorated and fitted out and the colour contrasts are not good, there is a lot you can do. For example you can put coloured transfers round the edges of sanitary wear such as the bath, just to highlight where they are or paint the part of the wall behind the toilet and sink in a contrasting colour to make them stand out.

10 hints on kitchens and dining rooms

1. Eating and drinking are important for health, and this especially is true if the person has dementia. There is sometimes a problem getting the person with dementia to want to eat, or they may only want small amounts. There are design features that you can incorporate in the kitchen and dining room that will help them with that. Keeping people involved with cooking is a great way to encourage them to eat. It might be that for some people, particularly older ladies, they maintain considerable skills from their lifetime of caring for others. You need to consider all the things at the start of the book about lighting, flooring and assistive technology, but you also need to think about specifics in this part of the house.

2. You will have justifiable anxieties about safety in the kitchen, and there is a great deal you can do to help with that. The kitchen is often seen as a place of great risk, but often the risks can be reduced with assistive technology as described in that section of this book. Total risk avoidance is severely limiting, and there is a serious discussion to be had about what level of risk is acceptable. However, before bringing any activity to an end it is worth checking if there are any reliable devices on the market that will reassure relatives or neighbours or anyone who might be anxious about the risk.

> Dad had a lovely next door neighbour who used to bring him a hot plate of whatever she was cooking for the family every day. I went to thank her for her kindness and her trouble and she said 'Anything is better than me having to think of him through that shared wall playing about with his cooker'.

3. The person with dementia has probably got memory loss and difficulty in working things out. You can help a lot by decluttering in the kitchen. Consider fitting units that are open fronted or have clear safety

10 hints on kitchens and dining rooms

glass so that food and cooking utensils can be seen. Open shelving is good and you can achieve that by just taking off the cupboard fronts. This means that the person does not have to search for the things that they will frequently need. Also have standard fronts on some cupboards to make them less visible or even lockable for higher risk equipment and cleaning materials. If you have them out of the way and invisible they are less likely to be used inappropriately.

4. Opt for traditional taps clearly marked with which is hot and which is cold. Hot water supplies need to be delivered at a safe temperature and be fitted with scald control valves. The principles here are the same as were outlined for the bathroom.

5. People with dementia may have a reduction in their appetite, but there are things that can be done to tempt them. If the person can always see the ingredients for making a cup of tea or coffee and having a biscuit, they are more likely to help themselves. A good level of light can help with this. A glass fronted fridge with nice food on show can tempt a person to eat and also allows others to see at a glance whether the food is being eaten and replaced with fresh produce, or mouldering on the shelves.

6. The table setting can make a difference to whether the person eats and drinks well. Tables need to be sturdy enough to support people who have mobility problems leaning on them. Clear leg space underneath makes them easier for wheelchair users, rounded edges and corners are safer, and they need to be high enough to prevent chairs with arms from getting jammed. You can get a dining chair with wooden sliders under the legs to aid the person in pulling their chair up to the table.

The person needs to see what is on their plate. Use of light is important in this context. As important is the contrast of the food to the plate. If the person cannot see the food then they may not be stimulated to eat. Mashed potatoes or white fish for example are things that may be hard to see on a white plate. A plate with a solid band round the outside may help food stand out.

Using crockery that the person recognises for its purpose may also be important. A big mug that the person has used over the last few years may no longer be recognised for its purpose. The person with dementia increasingly relies on earlier memories to do and make sense of things. A mug could even look like something that flowers should be placed in. If the person is not drinking enough think if there was a different type of cup or glass that they used in the past that they might recognise. Smaller design changes can help, so the colour of the tablecloth and the place mats contrasting with the plate is also useful.

Another simple tip with cups and cutlery is that putting the cup in someone's hand may stimulate the memory to lift it to their mouth. The glass or cup being set down in front of the person may not be enough to trigger the need to drink.

Coffee tables are often low and can be out of the field of vision. If the person with dementia is not drinking their tea and leave their sandwich or biscuits this may be because they cannot see them. Their coffee table may need replaced with a higher tray table that can be set more easily in their line of view.

7. Make sure that you take full advantage of all the devices that can be purchased which will help people with reduced mobility or strength to undertake kitchen tasks. For example there are simple devices that can help a person to open jars and bottle tops, levers that can be attached to taps to ease turning on and off, simple devices to hold pots and kettles so that the person does not have to take the full weight in their hands when moving them around in the kitchen.

8. Flood risks can be controlled in the kitchen by careful design of overflows and the use of automatic monitoring devices and plugs which allow the water to drain out when the sink is full. If the kitchen is fully fitted, the fridge and dishwasher may be hidden behind identical panels. You can help prevent confusion by placing a photograph on the outside of the door of what is behind the door when it is opened. Signs and labels can also help.

9. As described in the section on assistive technology, the person with dementia may benefit from a range of alarms, including CO, heat, smoke, flooding etc. However care should be taken that the alarm does not depend entirely on the person with dementia swiftly understanding that there is a problem, what it is, and what to do. This can be overcome by having alarms that are connected with a call centre or which alert a carer.

10. Your aim should be that the person can continue to make even quite simple meals for themselves for as long as possible, and for visitors. You have to be sure that your health and safety or food hygiene concerns don't take precedence over normal living. This can be helped with careful planning and paying attention to the available assistive technology.

10 hints on living areas

By living areas we mean internal spaces such as living rooms, halls and stairs, but also external spaces such as balconies and gardens. On each of these areas there are hints and ideas that are based on the basic principles at the start of this booklet.

1. A key feature of halls and stairs is that the person with dementia will be moving through them for a variety of purposes. Sometimes it will be at night when they may be tired and sleepy. Sometimes there will be some sort of urgency, as the person hurries to answer the door or to go to the toilet. The result of a fall can be very dangerous for an older person, so safety is paramount in these areas. Banisters or railings are best if they are on both sides of the stair. It is stating the obvious to point out the dangers of worn or loose carpets. Worn or loose footwear is equally dangerous.

2. Light is crucial, and as these areas are often not well lit everything should be done to maximise any daylight that is available. In addition care should be taken to make sure that any lights that are activated by movement sensors are activated in good time. If there is a slow sensor, too close to the stair, and the bulb takes time to rise to full light levels, there is a danger that the person will be half way up or down before they have enough light to see. For example, the hall light may be switched on by a movement sensor beside the bed.

3. Make light and power switches easy to see and operate. If the person needs to switch on a light to see what they are doing this can be a problem if the switch is hard to find. If the switch and wall plate are white and the wall is pale in colour, then the person may not notice it due to lack of contrast. This same problem can occur for the switch to turn on the kettle or a television. You can replace switches with contrasting switches or place a specially designed sticker over the light fitting. Alternatively, make sure the wall is painted a colour that contrasts with the switch and wall plate fitting.

4. When passing through the hall the person may be headed for the toilet, so making that place as clearly visible as possible can help. This might include labelling doors, or leaving the door open or the light on. If using signs make sure they are the right height for the person who needs to read it. We recommend that the base of the sign is no higher than 4 feet/122 cm from the floor. It might also be useful to make sure the toilet door is a different colour from the other doors and contrasts with the colour of the wall.

5. The general principles about contrast between walls and floors, and visibility of chairs and other furniture applies in living rooms and need not be laboured, as they are covered in the section about floor covering and decoration. As ever, maximising the light is very important.

6. Some areas of the house may become dangerous to the person, for example the hall cupboard that has chemicals in it or anything else that may cause danger. If these cannot be moved to another place, the area should be made as safe as possible. Painting the door of this cupboard the same colour as the wall may help to make it less obvious and not draw the person to it, especially if you paint a stripe on the bottom identical to the skirting board and recess the door handle.

7. Going into a garden is very good for people with dementia. For example, there is a clear connection between vitamin D levels and the danger of falls. If the person is able to spend time pottering in their garden, they will absorb sunlight which will keep them well. Daylight also helps to set the body clock and will therefore help them to sleep at night. A dementia friendly garden has a range of features which make it easy to use for the person with dementia, including flat paving for shuffling.

8. If the family is concerned about the person leaving the garden and becoming lost, it is possible to reduce the risk by having the right sort of fence or boundary. The gate in the fence can be made unobtrusive with planting or by putting the fastenings on the outside.

9. Having something to do in the garden is never a problem for keen gardeners as there is always weeding or digging or grass cutting to get on with. For those who are not gardeners there is always the chance to peg out some washing, sweep a path, or just sit and look at the world going by. One wonderful feature of a garden is that it gives the person with dementia the chance to demonstrate their skills to others. Many young people do not know how to pot up a plant or take a cutting and these are skills that can go on for a long time.

Even if you don't have a garden you can get a great deal of pleasure from a balcony with pot plants on it and a chair on which to sit and look out. A balcony is not automatically dangerous for people with dementia, depending on what they are used to, and the design of the balcony.

Conclusion

The person with dementia has a great deal to contend with as they start to have some difficulties in doing normal things over time. A lot of the difficulty can be anticipated and avoided with simple changes that can be made around the house.

Some of these ideas will be exactly what you need. Some people will read this and find nothing that helps. We would like to hear from you so that we can focus our work on searching out useful solutions to real problems.

Useful Reading

10 Helpful Hints for Carers: Practical solutions for carers living with people with dementia
ISBN: 978 1 85769 236 5   Dementia Services Development Centre

10 Helpful Hints for Carers is an easy-to-read guide for carers living with people with dementia. It provides simple, practical solutions to the everyday problems family carers can face when looking after a person with dementia. Covering areas like how to cope with aggression, creating relaxing environments, 'wandering', sleeplessness and how to cope with dementia and depression, it is a mine of information and good advice.

Best Practice in Design for People with Dementia
ISBN: 978 1 85769 247 1   Dementia Services Development Centre

This resource pack includes *Designing interiors for people with dementia, Designing lighting for people with dementia* and *Designing gardens for people with dementia*, as well as a Dementia design checklist to help you put the theory into practice. It reflects a growing awareness of the need to create caring environments that meet the needs of people with dementia. This pack can be used in conjunction with the DSDC's Design audit tool to help establish how suitable a building or other setting is for people with dementia.

Design for People with Dementia: Audit Tool
ISBN: 978 1 85769 229 7   Dementia Services Development Centre

The DSDC's design audit tool contains a series of resources for carrying out self-assessment of environments that are used by people with dementia. It is suitable for refurbishment projects or new buildings, and is relevant across a range of settings including day centres, wards, care homes and medical centres. The design audit tool will help identify areas for improvement, and can be used to prepare for the formal design audit certificate process.

Light and lighting design for people with dementia
ISBN: 978 1 85769 250 1   Dementia Services Development Centre

This accessible book explains how appropriate use of lighting can significantly help people with dementia better understand their environment. Published in association with the Institution of Lighting Engineers it includes many practical suggestions that involve minimal cost.

Living with Dementia: Adapting the home of a person who has Down's syndrome and dementia – a guide for carers
Down's Syndrome Scotland

People with dementia will be affected by changes in behaviour at different stages of their illness. This book is a collection of potential issues that you may come across in the home, with suggested solutions. The possible reasons for these changes are explained to give an insight into how dementia is experienced by people with Down's syndrome.

Telecare and dementia: using telecare effectively in the support of people with dementia
ISBN: 978 1 85769 246 4   Dementia Services Development Centre

This book explores how telecare can contribute to the support, protection and quality of life of people with dementia. It also considers the importance of telecare in providing support and reassurance to carers. This is one of a number of publications funded by the Scottish Government's National Telecare Development Programme, in pursuit of the strategic goal of raising awareness of the importance of telecare in contemporary health and social care services. To download other titles in the series free of charge visit http://www.dementiashop.co.uk/catalog/21

Useful reading

Organisations that can help

Always remember that help is at hand if through your GP or local social services if you care for a person with dementia. In addition here are some other organisations that might help:

Carers UK
20 Great Dover Street
London
SE1 4LX
020 7378 4999
http://www.carersuk.org

The Princess Royal Trust for Carers
Unit 14, Bourne Court
Southend Road, Woodford Green
Essex
IG8 8HD
0844 800 4361
http://www.carers.org

Counsel and Care
Twyman House
16 Bonny Street
London, NW1 9PG
020 7241 8555
http://www.counselandcare.org.uk

Alzheimer Scotland
22 Drumsheugh Gardens
Edinburgh
EH3 7RN
0131 243 1453
http://www.alzscot.org

Alzheimer's Society
Devon House
58 St Katharine's Way
London
EIW IJX
020 7423 3500
http://www.alzheimers.org.uk

Age UK
York House
207-211 Pentonville Road
London
N1 9UZ
0800 107 8977
http://www.ageuk.org.uk

The Relatives and Residents Association
24 The Ivories
6-18 Northampton Street
London
N1 2HY
020 7359 8136
http://www.relres.org

Carers Scotland
The Cottage, 21 Pearce Street
Glasgow
G51 3UT
0141 445 3070
http://www.carersscotland.org

Age NI

3 Lower Crescent
Belfast
BT7 1NR
028 9024 5729
http://www.ageuk.org.uk/northern-ireland

Alzheimer's Society Northern Ireland

Unit 4, Balmoral Business Park
Boucher Crescent
Belfast
BT12 6HU
028 9066 4100
http://www.alzheimers.org.uk

Age Cymru

13/14 Neptune Court
Vanguard Way
Cardiff
CF24 5PJ
http://www.ageuk.org.uk/cymru